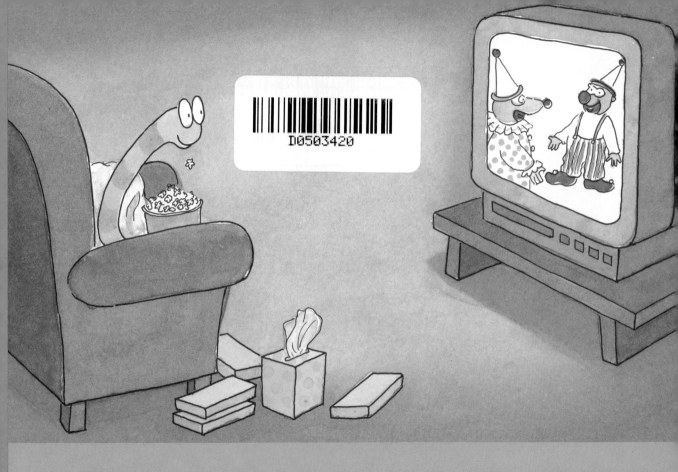

Worm watches a movie with clowns.

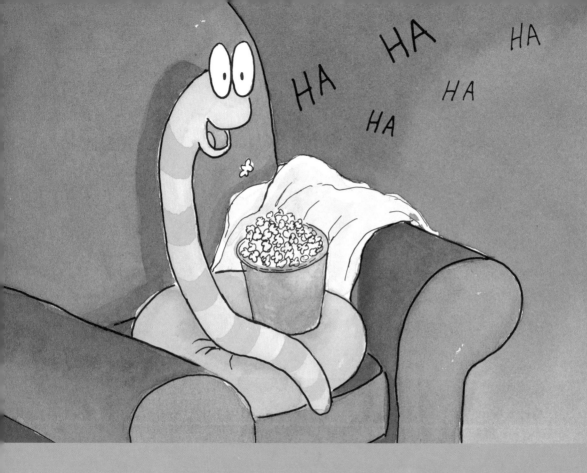

Worm laughs.

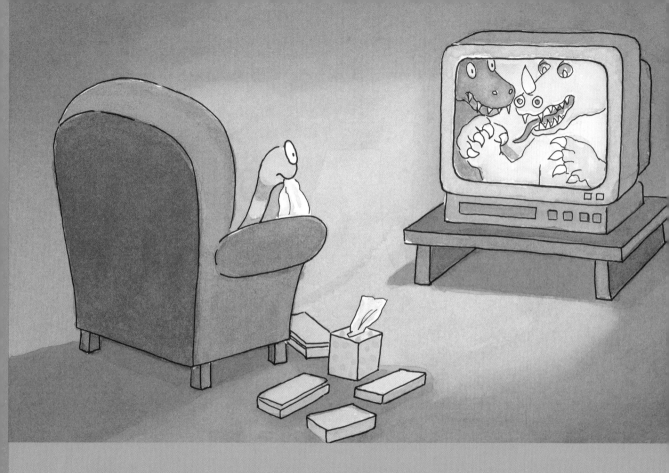

Worm watches a movie with monsters.

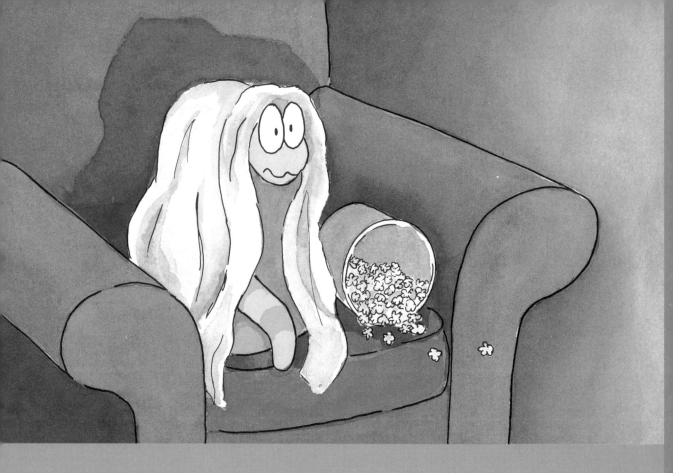

Worm hides.

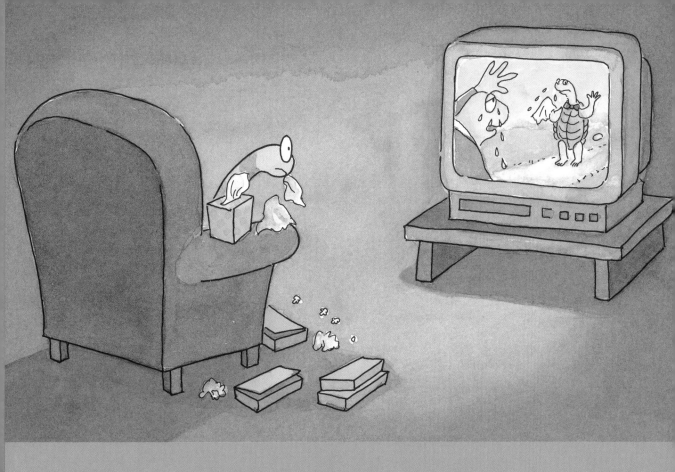

Worm watches a movie with crying.

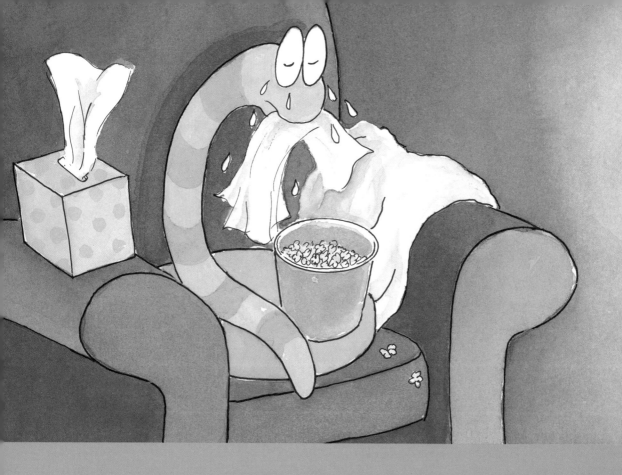

Worm cries.

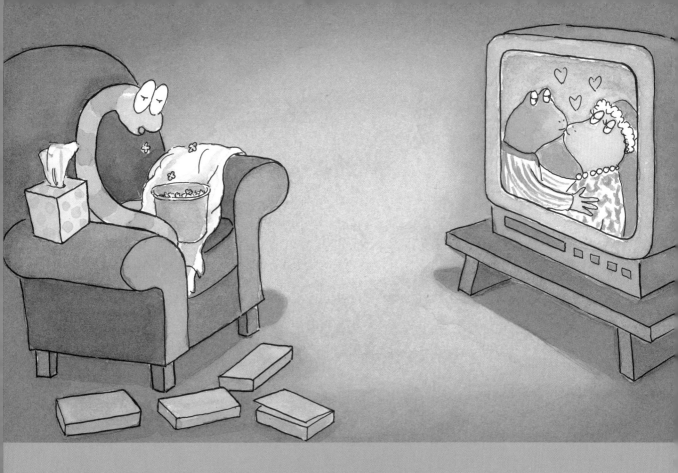

Worm watches a movie with kissing.

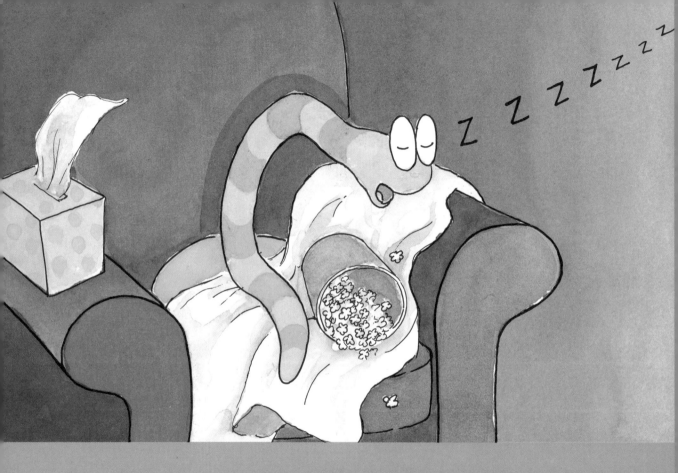

Worm falls asleep.